Usborne English Readers
Starter Level

KiNG MiDAS

Retold by Mairi Mackinnon
Illustrated by Paula Bossio

English language consultant: Peter Viney

Contents

You can listen to the story online here:
usborneenglishreaders.com/
kingmidas

This is the story of King Midas.
King Midas is very rich.
He loves gold.

I would like more gold.

Gold isn't everything.

One evening, a stranger comes to King Midas' palace.

Can I help you?

I'm lost.

"I'm looking for my friend," the stranger says. "He's near here somewhere."

"We can help you," says King Midas, "but it's dark now. Let's eat, and sleep. We can find your friend tomorrow."

They have a good meal, and they sleep well. In the morning, they soon find the man's friend.

"Oh!" says King Midas. "Your friend is a god!"

"He is," says the old man.

Dionysus, this is King Midas.

"King Midas is very kind," the old man tells Dionysus. "How can we say thank you?"

Dionysus says, "Well, King Midas, what do you want? You can ask for anything."

Anything?

Yes, anything. Remember, I'm a god.

King Midas thinks, "I can ask for gold – lots of gold."

Then he thinks "How can I make more gold?"

Then he thinks, "Can I change things into gold?"

"Dionysus," he says. "I want to change things into gold. I want to touch things and change them into gold."

"Really?" says Dionysus. "Do you want to change *everything*?"

"Yes, everything!" says King Midas.

Dionysus laughs. He touches King Midas's hands.

There. Now, touch something. Try it.

King Midas touches a tree. The tree changes. Now it's a gold tree. "Look at that!" says King Midas. "Thank you!"

He touches a flower. It changes into a gold flower. "Fantastic!" he says.

He goes back to his palace and opens the doors. "Look, gold doors!" he says.
He touches a table here, a chair there. "We have gold tables and chairs now." He sits down, then stands up quickly.

Hmm, gold chairs aren't comfortable.

King Midas is hungry. "Bring me some food," he says.

The palace servants bring food and put it on the gold table. King Midas takes some bread… but it's gold bread now. He can't eat it.

He takes an apple… and it's a gold apple. He can't eat anything.

His daughter comes in. "Father, what is all this gold?"

"No! Stop! Don't touch my hands!" says King Midas.

Now he has a gold daughter. He starts to cry.

He goes back to Dionysus. "I'm sorry," he says. "It's all a mistake. I don't want gold. I want my daughter. I want to eat. Can you change everything back again?"

"I can't change it for you," says Dionysus.

"There's a river near here," says Dionysus. "You need to wash your hands in it. Then wash your daughter in river water. Wash your food. Wash all your gold things."

"Thank you!" said King Midas.

He washes in the river. Then he touches a flower.

It doesn't change.

He brings some river water back to the palace. He washes his daughter, his food, the tables and chairs – everything.

"Thank you, Father," says his daughter. "No more gold."

Gold isn't everything.

About gold

Gold is a kind of metal.
People use gold to make different things.

Gold money

Kings and queens
have gold crowns.

Gold rings

Gold medals

Can you think of any other gold things?

Activities

The answers are on page 24.

Can you see these things in the picture?

Which three things *can't* you see?

animal   chair   daughter   flower

gold   god   king   palace

river   shoes   sun   tree

Is King Midas happy?

Choose the best answer.

1.

A. Yes. He loves his daughter.

B. Not really. He would like more gold.

2.

A. Yes. He has lots of gold now.

B. No. He wants his daughter and he's sorry.

3.

A. Yes. He doesn't need gold.

B. No. He can't make any more gold.

Ask, say, tell...

Choose the right word to finish each sentence.

ask	says	thinks	tells

1.

"King Midas is very kind," the old man .... Dionysus.

2.

"What do you want? You can .... for anything."

3.

He ...., "How can I make more gold?

4.

"Dionysus," he .... "I want to change things into gold."

What is King Midas thinking?

Choose the right words for each picture.

Oh no!

That's better!

What can I do?

Fantastic!

1.

2.

3.

4.

King Midas learns

Match the words to the pictures.

1.

2.

3.

4.

A. You can't eat gold bread.

B. Gold isn't everything.

C. Gods can do anything.

D. Gold chairs aren't comfortable.

Word list

apple (n) a round fruit, usually green or red, and white inside. Apples grow on trees.

comfortable (adj) when a chair or a bed is comfortable, it is a nice place to sit or lie down.

fantastic (adj) really good and special.

god (n) in stories, gods are very powerful and can do magic. They can live forever.

lost (adj) when you are lost, you don't know where you are or you can't find your way.

palace (n) the home of a king or queen.

servant

apple

river (n) water that is going towards the sea. Boats can go on rivers, and fish live in them.

servant (n) a person who works for another person in their home.

stranger (n) a person you don't know.

tomorrow (n) the day after today.

touch (v) when you touch something, you put your hand on it.

wash (v) to use water to make yourself or make something else clean.

touch

Answers

Can you see these things in the picture?

Three things you can't see: chair, daughter, palace.

Is King Midas happy?

B, B, A

Ask, say, tell...

1. tells
2. ask
3. thinks
4. says

What is King Midas thinking?

1. D
2. A
3. C
4. B

King Midas learns

1. C
2. D
3. A
4. B

You can find information about other Usborne English Readers here: usborneenglishreaders.com

Designed by Samantha Barrett

Edited by Jane Chisholm

First published in 2020 by Usborne Publishing Ltd.,
Usborne House, 83-85 Saffron Hill, London EC1N 8RT, England.
usborne.com Copyright © 2020 Usborne Publishing Ltd.